That dwells in sha - dows? Do not for - get__ me
oh
O - - - - - - - - - - - -

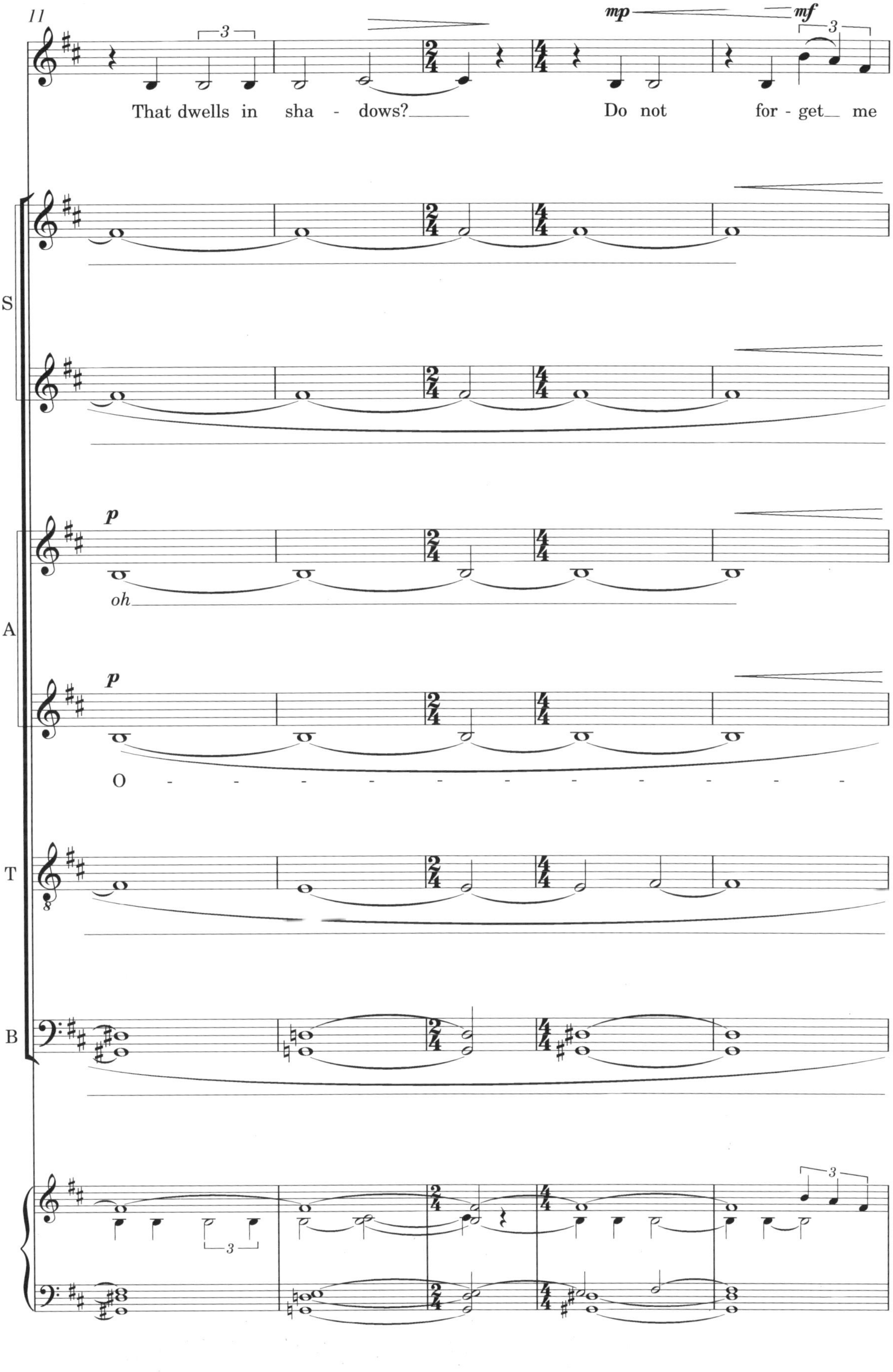

16
quite.
S
mf
O - nly the wan - der-er Knows Eng - land's grace,
mf
_(O) - nly the wan - der-er Knows Eng - land's gra -
A
mf
O - nly_ the_ wan - der-er Knows Eng - land's gra -
mf
- - nly_ the_ wan - der-er Knows Eng - land's grace,___
T
mf
Eng - land's
(O) - nly the wan - der-er Knows Eng - land's grace,___
B
mf
grace,
(O) - nly the wan - der-er Knows Eng - land's gra -

**BOOSEY & HAWKES
CONTEMPORARY CHORAL SERIES**

Briggs: *Severn Meadows*
Soprano solo & SATB (with divisi) a cappella

MIXED VOICES

DIFFICULTY: ★★★★☆

Kerensa Briggs

Severn Meadows

for soprano solo & SATB (with divisi) a cappella

Maximum divisi SSAATTBB

Composer's note

Severn Meadows was commissioned for Cantores Chamber Choir in 2022 and is dedicated to Kate, Simon and Florence Harper. The words are taken from Ivor Gurney's song of the same name, which is likely to have been written in the trenches of the First World War in 1917. It also takes musical influence from Gurney, as well as Gerald Finzi, both of whom were local to the Gloucestershire countryside for which the text expresses a love and longing.

Duration: *c*4½ minutes

Text

Only the wanderer
Knows England's graces,
Or can anew see clear
Familiar faces.

And who loves joy as he
That dwells in shadows?
Do not forget me quite,
O Severn meadows.

Kerensa Briggs

Kerensa Briggs is an award-winning composer specialising in choral music. Described as "poignant, ambivalent, quietly devastating music" in the New York Times, her works have been performed internationally at venues including St Paul's Cathedral, London and the Sistine Chapel, Vatican City. Her music is regularly performed or broadcast with groups such as VOCES8, The Sixteen and the BBC Singers. Her portrait disc *Requiem* (2023) on Delphian Records placed in the top 30 classical charts and was described as "alluring and heartfelt music" by BBC Music Magazine. Kerensa was winner of the National Centre for Early Music Young Composers Award 2014 and is an alumna of the TheoArtistry Composers scheme at St Andrews' Institute for Theology and the Arts. She is currently Composer in Residence for St Louis Chamber Chorus. Her love of choral music emanates from her background, singing in choirs including Gloucester Cathedral Youth and the choir of King's College London, where she held a Choral Scholarship and undertook an MMus in Composition.

Published by Boosey & Hawkes Music Publishers Ltd
Aldwych House, 71–91 Aldwych, London WC2B 4HN
© Copyright 2025 by Boosey & Hawkes Music Publishers Ltd
ISMN 979-0-060-15136-1, ISBN 978-1-83568-086-5
First impression 2025
Printed by Halstan:
Halstan UK, 2–10 Plantation Road, Amersham, Bucks, HP6 6HJ, United Kingdom
Halstan DE, Johannes-Kepler-Straße 5, 55129 Mainz, Germany
Music setting derived from the composer's original by Jon Bunker

for Kate, Simon and Florence Harper

SEVERN MEADOWS

IVOR GURNEY
(1890–1937)

KERENSA BRIGGS
(b 1991)

as he
-dows, O Se - vern mea - dow.
- dows, O do not for - get me.
- dows, O do not for - get,
- dows, O Se - vern mea - dow.
-dows, O Se - vern mea - dow.

cresc poco a poco
Or can a - new see clear Fa - mi - liar fa - ces.
-ces, Or can a-new see clear Fa-mi - liar fa - ces, the
-ces, O - nly the wan -
cresc poco a poco
Or can a - new see clear Fa - mi - liar fa - ces,
cresc poco a poco
Or can a - new see clear Fa - mi - liar fa - ces,
cresc poco a poco
Or can a - new see clear Fa - mi - liar fa - ces,
cresc poco a poco
-ces, new see clear Fa - mi - liar, O - nly the

poco rit
26
mf
f
O - nly the wan-der-er knows Eng - land's gra - ces.
S
wan - der - er, the wan-der-er knows Eng - land's gra - ces.
- der - er, the wan-der-er knows Eng - land's gra - ces.
A
the wan-der-er knows Eng - land's gra - ces.
O - nly the wan-der-er knows Eng - land's gra - ces.
T
cresc poco a poco
O - nly the wan - der - er, the wan-der-er knows Eng - land's gra - ces.
B
wan - der-er knows Eng - land, the wan-der-er knows Eng - land's gra - ces.
poco rit

a tempo
Do not for - get me quite, O Se -
Do not for - get me quite, O Se -
Do not for - get me quite, O do not for -
quite, O Se -
Do not for - get me quite, O Se -
a tempo
Se - vern
-vern mea - dows, O do not for - get me
- vern mea - dows, O Se - vern
-get, Se-vern mea - dows, O Se - vern
- vern mea - dows, O Se - vern
- vern mea - dows, O Se - vern

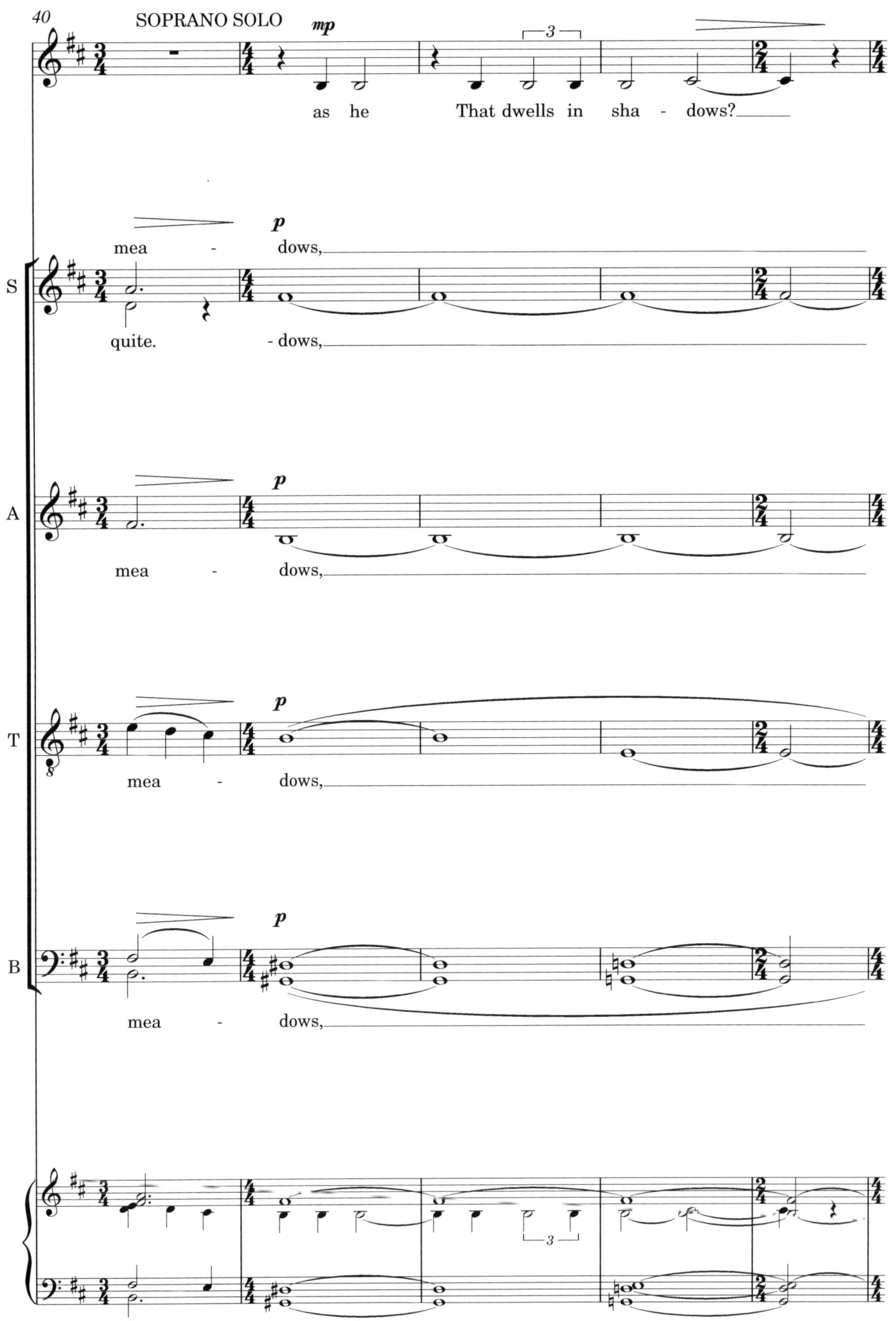
40
SOPRANO SOLO
mp
3
as he
That dwells in sha - dows?
mea - dows,
p
quite.
- dows,
S
mea - dows,
p
A
mea - dows,
p
T
mea - dows,
p
B
mea - dows,
3

Do not for - get_____ me quite,
Do not for - get_____ me, Se-vern mea-
Do not for -
Do not for - get_____ me,_____
Do not for - get_____ me, Se - vern mea-

50
S
- dows.
and who loves joy as he That
- dows.
And who loves joy,
A
And who loves joy, and who loves joy, That
- get, who loves joy, and who loves joy as he That dwells
T
And who loves joy as he,
B
And who loves joy, as he That
- dows.
And who loves joy as he That

poco rit
55
mf
dwells in sha - dows? Do not for-get me
mf
Do not for - get me, for - get me
dwells in sha-dows? Do not for - get,
in sha-dows? for - get me
in sha - dows? Do not for-get me quite, do not for-get me
dwells in sha - dows? Do not for - get me
poco rit

a tempo
rit
SOPRANO SOLO
59
mf
f
mf
O Se - vern mea - dows, O Se - vern,
quite, Se-vern mea - dows.
quite, Se - vern mea - dows, O Se -
Se - vern mea - dows, O Se -
quite, Se - vern mea - dows, O Se -
quite, Se - vern mea - dows, O do not for - get,
quite, Se - vern mea - dows, O Se -
a tempo
rit

as he That dwells in sha - dows?
Do not for - get, sha - dows?
- vern mea - dows. sha - dows?
- vern mea - dows.
Se-vern mea - dows, as he That dwells in sha - dows?
- vern mea - dows,
- vern mea - dows,

BH 15136

BOOSEY & HAWKES

Boosey & Hawkes Music Publishers Ltd
www.boosey.com

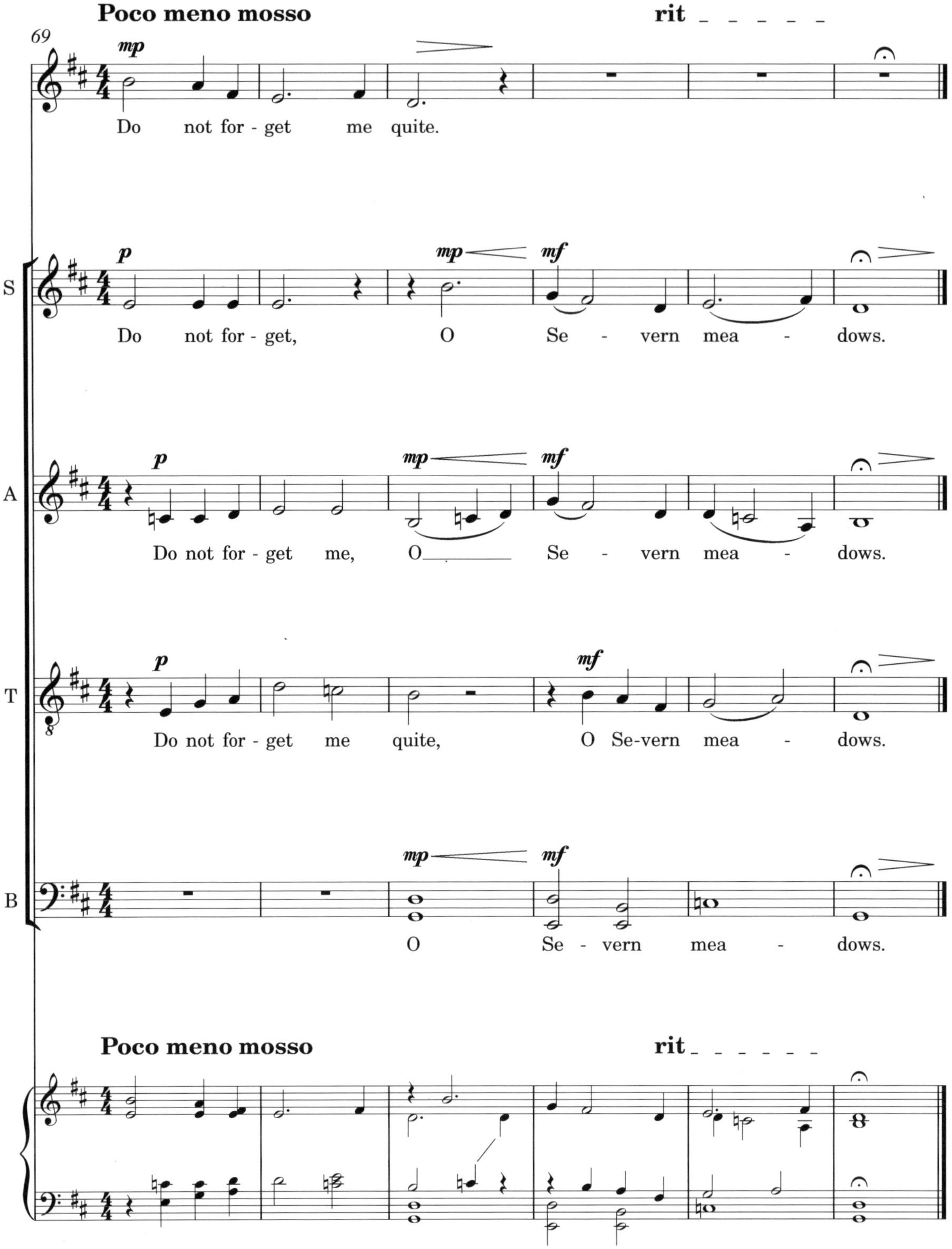

ISBN 978-1-83568-086-5

ISMN 979-0-060-15136-1